T0286421

Easy Concert Pieces
Leichte Konzertstücke

for Violin and Piano
für Violine und Klavier

Volume 3 / Band 3

16 Famous Pieces from 4 Centuries
16 beliebte Stücke aus 4 Jahrhunderten

(mittelschwer/intermediate)

Edited by / Herausgegeben von
Peter Mohrs

ED 22550
ISMN 979-0-001-16095-7
ISBN 978-3-7957-1024-8

Cover illustration:
Light cone: © PRO Bilder – Fotolia.com

Volume 1 / Band 1:
Very easy / sehr leicht
ED 21633

Volume 2 / Band 2:
Easy / leicht
ED 21634

Mainz · London · Berlin · Madrid · New York · Paris · Prague · Tokyo · Toronto
© 2018 SCHOTT MUSIC GmbH & Co. KG, Mainz · Printed in Germany

Preface

The "Easy Concert Pieces" series for Violin and Piano contains pieces at easy to intermediate standard ranging from the Baroque to the Modern era and carefully selected for their technical and musical features. These pieces are intended for tuition purposes and are particularly suitable for performance at auditions and school concerts, for competitions, examinations - and for music making at home too, of course.

Following on from Volume 1 (very easy) and Volume 2 (easy), where all the pieces can be played in 1st position, Volume 3 (intermediate) requires familiarity with the first four positions.

Most of the pieces are original compositions for violin. Besides well-known works such as the famous *Air* by Bach, *Largo* from Handel's opera 'Xerxes' and a movement from Vivaldi's *Four Seasons*, there are rewarding concerto and sonata movements by Küchler and Fiocco, as well as less familiar Romantic compositions by Rieding and Trowell. Modern music is represented in two lovely pieces by Hermann Schroeder, also inspired by the theme of the seasons. Young violinists are sure to enjoy the four pop pieces that round off the selection.

A CD is included to help with learning these pieces. It offers an opportunity to develop familiarity by listening to the pieces; then separately recorded piano accompaniments allow students to try playing along with the piano part. The CD recording was kindly made by Prof. Benjamin Bergmann (violin) and Leonid Dorfman (piano).

Have fun with your playing as you enjoy a journey through musical history!

Vorwort

Die Reihe „Easy Concert Pieces" für Violine und Klavier enthält leichte bis mittelschwere Kompositionen von der Barockzeit bis zur Moderne, die sorgfältig nach technischen und musikalischen Gesichtspunkten ausgewählt wurden. Die Stücke sind für den Unterricht gedacht und eignen sich besonders für Vorspiele an Musikschulen, für Wettbewerbe und Prüfungen und natürlich auch für das Musizieren zu Hause.

Nach Band 1 (sehr leicht) und Band 2 (leicht), deren Stücke allesamt in der 1. Lage spielbar sind, verlangt der vorliegende Band 3 (mittelschwer) die Kenntnisse der ersten vier Lagen. Die Ansprüche an Geläufigkeit, Griff- und Bogentechnik sowie an das Gestalten der Musik sind gestiegen.

Der überwiegende Teil der Stücke sind Originalwerke für Violine. Neben bekannten Werken wie der berühmten *Air* von Bach und dem *Largo* aus der Oper „Xerxes" von Händel sowie einem Satz aus Vivaldis *Vier Jahreszeiten*, gibt es dankbare Konzert- und Sonatensätze von Küchler und Fiocco sowie unbekanntere romantische Kompositionen von Rieding und Trowell. Die Moderne ist vertreten durch zwei schöne Sätze von Hermann Schroeder, die ebenfalls dem Thema „Jahreszeiten" gewidmet sind. Besondere Freude werden den jungen Geigerinnen und Geigern sicher die vier Stücke im Popstil machen, die das Heft abrunden.

Das Einstudieren der Stücke wird durch die beiliegende CD erleichtert. Sie bietet zum einen die Möglichkeit, die Stücke vorweg anzuhören und kennen zu lernen. Zum anderen bekommt man mittels der separat aufgenommenen Klavierbegleitungen die Gelegenheit, Erfahrungen im Zusammenspiel zu sammeln. Die Einspielung der CD wurde dankenswerter Weise von Herrn Prof. Benjamin Bergmann (Violine) und Leonid Dorfman (Klavier) übernommen.

Nun wünsche ich viel Spaß beim Spielen und eine spannende Reise durch die Musikgeschichte.

Peter Mohrs

Contents / Inhalt

		Piano	Violin	Track
Johann Sebastian Bach (1685-1750)	Air from/aus: Orchestral Suite No. 3, BWV 1068	4	4	1/17
Georg Friedrich Händel (1685-1759)	Largo from/aus: Xerxes	6	5	2/18
Ferdinand Küchler (1867-1937)	Concertino in the style of Antonio Vivaldi / im Stil von Antonio Vivaldi, op. 15			
	1 Allegro moderato	8	6	3/19
	2 Siciliano	12	8	4/20
	3 Allegro assai	13	8	5/21
Antonio Vivaldi (1678-1741)	Largo from/aus: The Four Seasons / Die vier Jahreszeiten (Winter)	16	9	6/22
	Allegro from/aus: Concerto in G major / G-Dur, op. 3/3	18	10	7/23
Joseph-Hector Fiocco (1703-1741)	Allegro	24	12	8/24
Oskar Rieding (1840-1918)	Gypsies' March / Zigeunermarsch op. 23/2	28	14	9/25
Arnold Trowell (1873-1966)	Irish Lullaby, op. 49/2	32	16	10/26
Hermann Schroeder (1904-1984)	Autumn Melody / Herbstweise from/aus: The four Seasons / Die vier Jahreszeiten . . .	34	17	11/27
	Winter Storm / Wintersturm from/aus: The four Seasons / Die vier Jahreszeiten . . .	36	18	12/28
Peter Mohrs (*1956)	Meditation	38	19	13/29
Joachim Johow (*1952)	Hello Violin	40	20	14/30
Gabriel Koeppen (*1958)	Yellow Bossa	43	22	15/31
Daniel Kemminer (*1978)	Malapata / Unlucky Fellow / Pechvogel	46	23	16/32
	Tuning note / Stimmton (a = 442 Hz)			33

Air

from the Orchestral Suite No. 3 D major
aus der Orchestersuite Nr. 3 D-Dur

BWV 1068

Johann Sebastian Bach
1685–1750
Arr.: Wolfgang Birtel

Violine

Klavier

Largo

Georg Friedrich Händel
1685–1759
Arr.: Wolfgang Lichter

from the opera "Serses" / aus der Oper „Xerxes"

Concertino
in the style of Antonio Vivaldi
im Stil von Antonio Vivaldi
opus 15

Ferdinand Küchler
1867–1937

I

58

62

II Siciliano

Larghetto (♪ ca. 82)

5

attacca subito

III Allegro assai

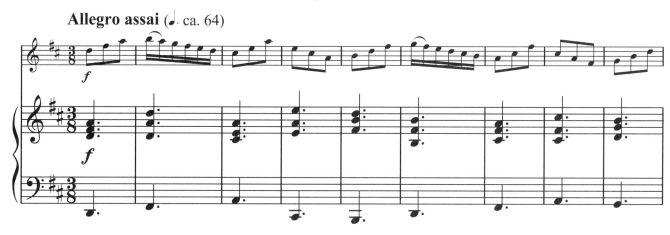

Largo

from / aus: „Winter"

Antonio Vivaldi
1678–1741
Arr.: Wolfgang Lichter

from / aus: The Four Seasons / Die vier Jahreszeiten, op. 8/4

Allegro
opus 3/3

Antonio Vivaldi
1678–1741
Arr.: Wolfgang Lichter

from / aus: Concerto G major / G-Dur, op. 3/3 ("L'estro armonico")

Aus wendetechnischen Gründen bleibt diese Seite frei.
This page is left blank to save an unnecessary page turn.

Allegro

Joseph Hector Fiocco
1703–1741
Arr.: Rainer Mohrs

original: J. H. Fiocco, Pièces des clavecin, Première Suite (Allegro)

Easy Concert Pieces
Leichte Konzertstücke

for Violin and Piano
für Violine und Klavier

Volume 3 / Band 3

16 Famous Pieces from 4 Centuries
16 beliebte Stücke aus 4 Jahrhunderten

(mittelschwer/intermediate)

Edited by / Herausgegeben von
Peter Mohrs

ED 22550
ISMN 979-0-001-16095-7
ISBN 978-3-7957-1024-8

Volume 1 / Band 1:
Very easy / sehr leicht
ED 21633

Volume 2 / Band 2:
Easy / leicht
ED 21634

Violin

Mainz · London · Berlin · Madrid · New York · Paris · Prague · Tokyo · Toronto
© 2018 SCHOTT MUSIC GmbH & Co. KG, Mainz · Printed in Germany

Contents / Inhalt

		Piano	Violin	Track
Johann Sebastian Bach (1685-1750)	Air from/aus: Orchestral Suite No. 3, BWV 1068	4	4	1/17
Georg Friedrich Händel (1685-1759)	Largo from/aus: Xerxes	6	5	2/18
Ferdinand Küchler (1867-1937)	Concertino in the style of Antonio Vivaldi / im Stil von Antonio Vivaldi, op. 15			
	1 Allegro moderato.	8	6	3/19
	2 Siciliano.	12	8	4/20
	3 Allegro assai.	13	8	5/21
Antonio Vivaldi (1678-1741)	Largo from/aus: The Four Seasons / Die vier Jahreszeiten (Winter)	16	9	6/22
	Allegro from/aus: Concerto in G major / G-Dur, op. 3/3	18	10	7/23
Joseph-Hector Fiocco (1703-1741)	Allegro	24	12	8/24
Oskar Rieding (1840-1918)	Gypsies' March / Zigeunermarsch op. 23/2	28	14	9/25
Arnold Trowell (1873-1966)	Irish Lullaby, op. 49/2	32	16	10/26
Hermann Schroeder (1904-1984)	Autumn Melody / Herbstweise from/aus: The four Seasons / Die vier Jahreszeiten . . .	34	17	11/27
	Winter Storm / Wintersturm from/aus: The four Seasons / Die vier Jahreszeiten . . .	36	18	12/28
Peter Mohrs (*1956)	Meditation	38	19	13/29
Joachim Johow (*1952)	Hello Violin.	40	20	14/30
Gabriel Koeppen (*1958)	Yellow Bossa.	43	22	15/31
Daniel Kemminer (*1978)	Malapata / Unlucky Fellow / Pechvogel.	46	23	16/32
	Tuning note / Stimmton (a = 442 Hz)			33

Air
from the Orchestral Suite No. 3 D major
aus der Orchestersuite Nr. 3 D-Dur
BWV 1068

Johann Sebastian Bach
1685–1750

Largo

Georg Friedrich Händel
1685–1759

from the opera "Serses" / „aus der Oper Xerxes"

Concertino
in the style of Antonio Vivaldi
im Stil von Antonio Vivaldi
opus 15

I

Ferdinand Küchler
1867–1937

II Siciliano

III Allegro assai

Largo

from / aus: "Winter"

Antonio Vivaldi
1678–1741

from / aus: The Four Seasons / Die vier Jahreszeiten op. 8/4

Allegro

opus 3/3

Antonio Vivaldi
1678–1741

© 2018 Schott Music GmbH & Co. KG, Mainz

from / aus: Concerto G major / G-Dur, op. 3/3 ("L'estro armonico")

Allegro

Joseph Hector Fiocco
1703–1741

Gypsies' March / Zigeuner-Marsch

opus 23/2

Oskar Rieding
1840–1918

Irish Lullaby

opus 49/2

Arnold Trowell
1873–1966

Andante con moto (♪ ca. 96)

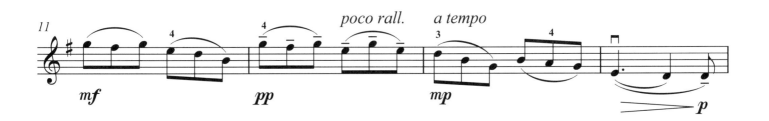

Autumn Melody / Herbstweise

Hermann Schroeder
1904–1984

from / aus: H. Schroeder, The Four Seasons / Die vier Jahreszeiten, Schott ED 21676

Winter Storm / Wintersturm

Hermann Schroeder
1904–1984

from / aus: H. Schroeder, The Four Seasons / Die vier Jahreszeiten, Schott ED 21676

Meditation

Peter Mohrs
*1956

Hello Violin

Joachim Johow
*1952

from / aus: J. Johow, My blue Violin, Schott ED 21767

Yellow Bossa

Gabriel Koeppen
*1958

Malapata
Unlucky Fellow / Pechvogel

Daniel Kemminer
*1978

Schott Music, Mainz 57 578

D. S. al Fine

Gypsies' March / Zigeuner-Marsch

opus 23/2

Oskar Rieding
1840–1918

Irish Lullaby

opus 49/2

Arnold Trowell
1873–1966

Andante con moto (♪ ca. 96)

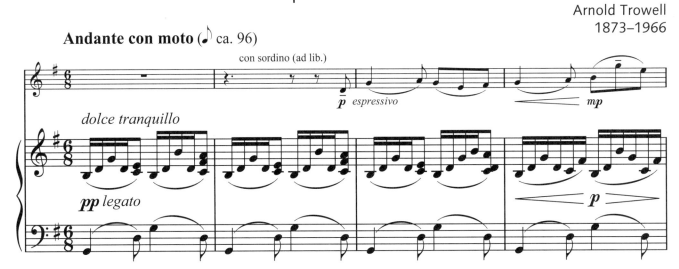

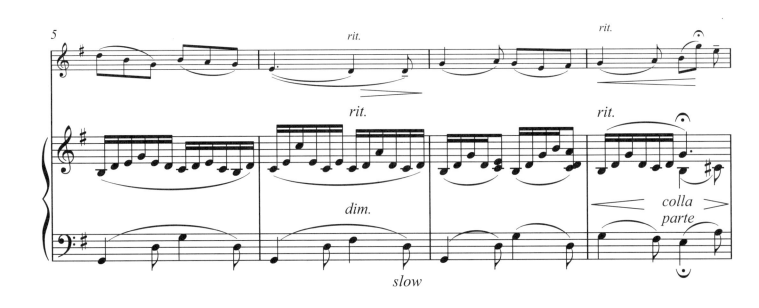

Autumn Melody / Herbstweise

Hermann Schroeder
1904–1984

from / aus: H. Schroeder, The Four Seasons / Die vier Jahreszeiten, Schott ED 21676

Winter Storm / Wintersturm

Hermann Schroeder
1904–1984

from / aus: H. Schroeder, The Four Seasons / Die vier Jahreszeiten, Schott ED 21676

Meditation

Peter Mohrs
*1956

Hello Violin

Joachim Johow
*1952

from / aus: J. Johow, My blue Violin, Schott ED 21767

Yellow Bossa

Gabriel Koeppen
*1958

44

Malapata
Unlucky Fellow / Pechvogel

Daniel Kemminer
*1978

Tempo di Tango (♩ ca. 124)

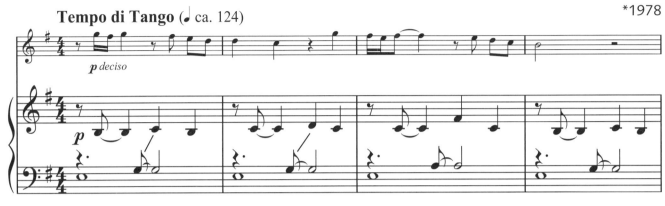

48